Monsters From t

Introduction

There are loads of monsters flying about.
While we eat our breakfasts they are out there —
soaring, snarling, munching and screeching.

This book covers four of these beasts from the sky.

The Moon Crow is like a beefed up dragon.
The Cloud Squid hides in the clouds, munching birds.
Microbats feed on thoughts in human brains.
The Hilltongue slurps with ten thousand tongues.

Published by CGP

Contents

The Moon Crow

The Moon Crow looks like a big, grinning dragon with a pointy head.

Heatproof scales
The scales stop the Moon Crow burning when it flies through the Earth.

A very hard head
This makes the Moon Crow good at bashing through rock.

Massive wings
These are strong enough to carry the Moon Crow faster than a bullet.

Pointy red face

Hungry belly
The Moon Crow only eats once in its whole life.

Lots of teeth
These are great for smiling in pictures and for ripping apart Giant Sea Slugs.

Long tail
This helps the Moon Crow swim through the sea.

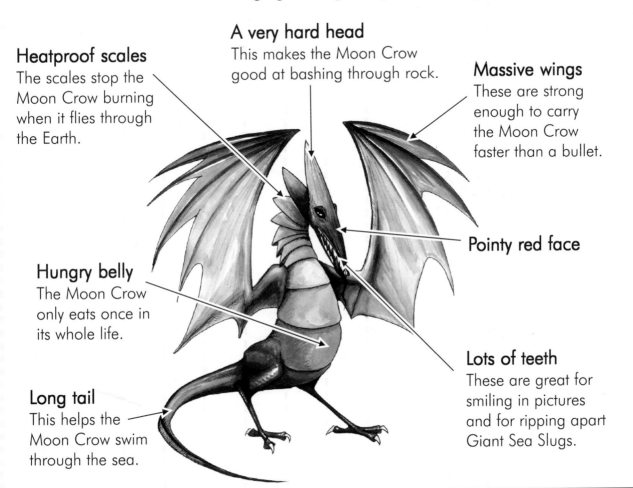

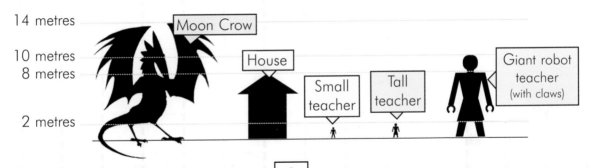

14 metres

10 metres
8 metres

2 metres

Moon Crow

House

Small teacher

Tall teacher

Giant robot teacher (with claws)

The Moon Crow

Food

Moon Crows eat Giant Sea Slugs. These are ugly things that live underwater

Unbreakable scales
Even a Moon Crow can't break these.

One massive eye
This eye is the same size as a large whale.

Large whale

Spiky tail
The spikes are as sharp as razors.

Soft belly
This is the Giant Sea Slug's weakness.
That's why it keeps its belly hidden.

Enemies

Moon Crows can get chewed into pieces by an Anything Eel.

Horrible hairy tail
If an Anything Eel sees its own tail it will eat itself.

Tiny brain
Anything Eels just eat everything, they don't need to think.

Very sharp teeth
The teeth slice through anything that's bitten.

Find out more about the Giant Sea Slug and the Anything Eel in the book "Monsters from the Sea".

Tail light
The light helps the Anything Eel find food at night.

Huge mouth
Anything goes in.
Nothing comes out.

The Moon Crow

Catching Food

Moon Crows have to be clever to get past the Giant Sea Slug's scales.

Moon Crows can't attack Giant Sea Slugs from above because their scales are too hard. Giant Sea Slugs have to be hit from underneath.

1. The Giant Sea Slug only breaks wind once in its life. When it does, it's the most disgusting smell in the world.

2. Giant Sea Slug wind is so stinky, the Moon Crow can smell it from the sky on the other side of the Earth.

3. The Moon Crow rockets towards the ground at top speed. Its legs and wings drop off to give it maximum speed.

4. The Moon Crow hits the ground and zooms straight through the Earth. It comes out underneath the Giant Sea Slug.

5. The Moon Crow hits the Giant Sea Slug from underneath, bursting its soft belly.

(It takes twenty years for the Moon Crow to eat the Giant Sea Slug. When it's finished, both wings and both legs have grown back.)

1 slug wind

2 sniffing — sniff sniff sniff

3 losing wings and legs

4 diving through the Earth

5 BULLSEYE

The Moon Crow

Life cycle

This comic strip shows the life of a Moon Crow.

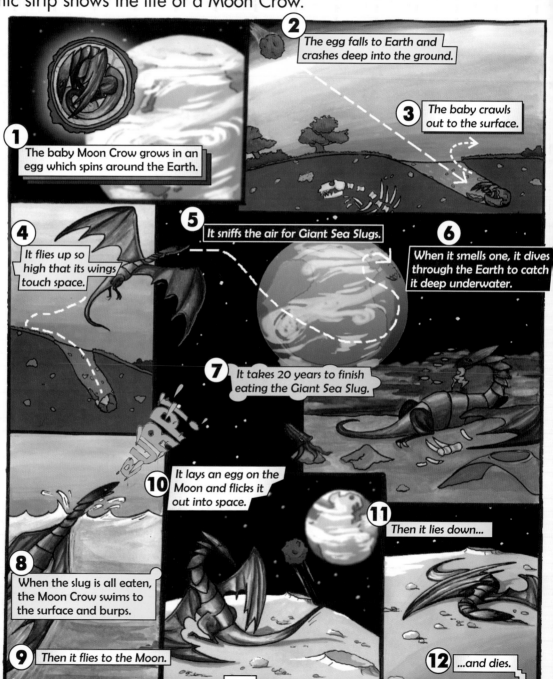

The Moon Crow

How to Spot One

Moon Crows fly so fast, you only have three chances to see one.

First chance to spot a Moon Crow:

When they come out of the ground after hatching from an egg.

Second chance to spot a Moon Crow:

When they are at the bottom of the sea. They are so deep you'll need a submarine. (Yuk! It's eating an eye.)

Third chance to a spot Moon Crow:

If a Moon Crow gets the dive wrong it makes a right mess. The mess and the crater make it easy to spot.

DANGER

WARNING
Be careful if you see one of these alive.
If it sees you, it might not be very polite.

The Cloud Squid

The Cloud Squid

Not all clouds are fluffy and nice. Some of them are great big monsters.

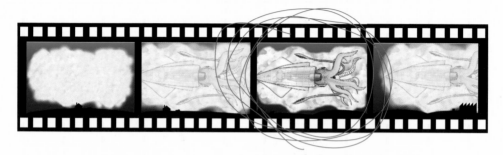

The Cloud Squid makes its own cloud to hide in.

It has two massive eyes to spot birds.

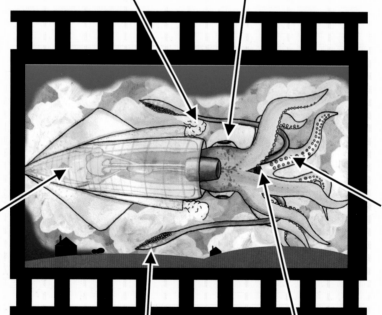

The Cloud Squid's body is filled with gas to make it float.

All eight tentacles smell of bread and fish.

The Cloud Squid has two long arms to pull birds into its mouth.

In the middle of the tentacles is a mouth. It's big, round and full of sharp teeth.

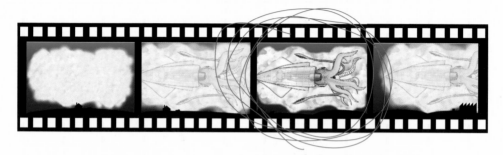

The Cloud Squid

Food

Cloud Squids eat flocks of birds. The more the merrier.

Sensible bird
She might not get munched at the back.

Are we there yet?

honk

honk

Stupid bird
She's going to be munched first if the flock flies into a Cloud Squid.

Enemies

Nothing eats Cloud Squids, but they get minced into tiny bits if they hit a jet or a helicopter.

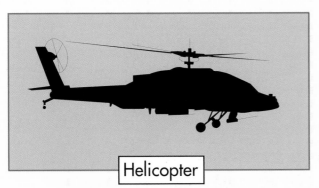

Helicopter

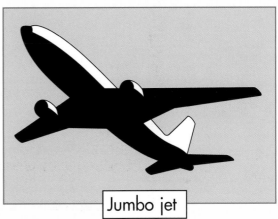

Jumbo jet

"It takes ages to clean your plane if you hit a squiddy."

The Cloud Squid

Catching Food

Cloud Squids love flocks of birds. They munch them up, feathers and all.

Cloud Squids smell like breadcrumbs and bits of fish.

smell   smell
smell   smell

Birds like the smell, so they fly towards what they think is a cloud.

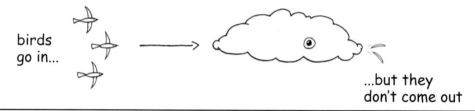

birds go in...

...but they don't come out

The arms of the Cloud Squid pull the birds into its giant mouth.

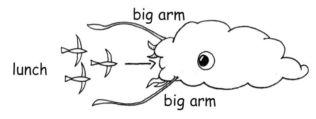

big arm

lunch

big arm

If they get really hungry, Cloud Squids drift down in fog and eat sheep and cows.

she senses danger

she didn't sense danger

The Cloud Squid

Life Cycle

Not many people notice the quiet life of the Cloud Squid.

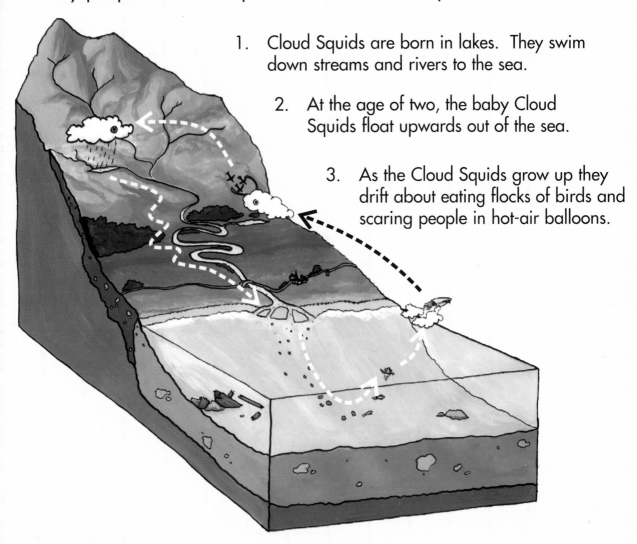

1. Cloud Squids are born in lakes. They swim down streams and rivers to the sea.

2. At the age of two, the baby Cloud Squids float upwards out of the sea.

3. As the Cloud Squids grow up they drift about eating flocks of birds and scaring people in hot-air balloons.

4. When they are nineteen, Cloud Squids lay eggs. The eggs fall like hail over the mountains.

5. Cloud Squids die when they get bored of eating birds.

clever sheep

The Cloud Squid

How to Spot One

This is a diary page from the notebook of a Cloud Squid spotter.

Tuesday, 25th May, 2004

I got up early to go squid spotting.

At 8.30am I saw a flock of birds flying round a big cloud.

They flew into the cloud and didn't come out.
I knew it must be a CLOUD SQUID!!

I flew my yellow kite up towards it.

A giant arm grabbed the kite and pulled it into the cloud.

I heard a loud munching sound.

At 3pm I went home to make a new kite.

blood stain?

maybe ketchup

tea stain

15 m

60 m

The Microbat

Microbats are tiny, but that doesn't mean they're nice.

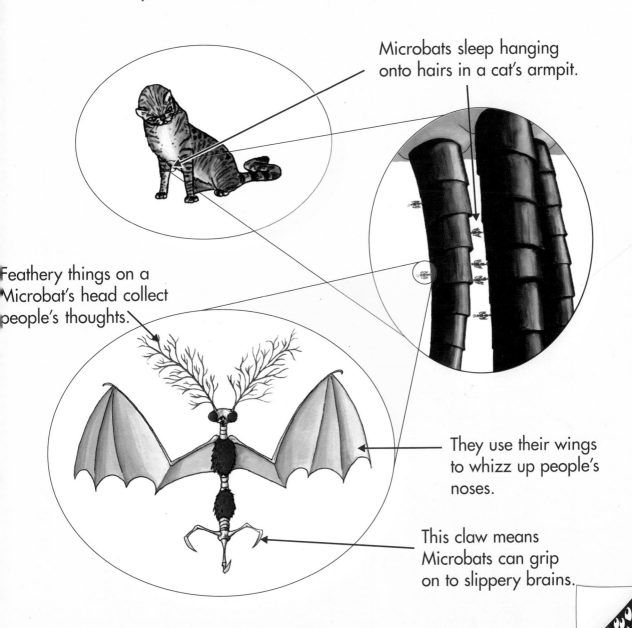

Microbats sleep hanging onto hairs in a cat's armpit.

Feathery things on a Microbat's head collect people's thoughts.

They use their wings to whizz up people's noses.

This claw means Microbats can grip on to slippery brains.

The Microbat

Food

It sounds odd, but Microbats eat thoughts from human brains.

They suck up our thoughts before we know what's going on.

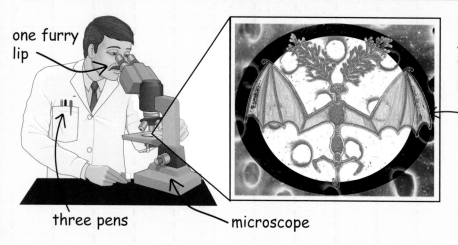

one furry lip

three pens

microscope

A Microbat uses the big feathery things on its head to suck up thoughts

This orange glow happens when the Microbat is stuffed full of thoughts.

Enemies

Anyone that eats their own snot is an enemy of the Microbat.

Microbats enter brains through the nose, but sometimes they get stuck in the snot. If the snot is picked, rolled and flicked the Microbats can escape, but if the snot is eaten the Microbats die.

TOO DISGUSTING

We were asked to cover up the diagrams in this section. They were too disgusting and might encourage people to pick their noses. Don't do it — Microbats taste horrible.

The Microbat

Catching Food

Microbats fly into brains and suck out the thoughts.

STAGE 1
Microbats fly around in swarms looking for noses.
They're like bees looking for nectar in flowers.

STAGE 2
The swarm of Microbats fly up a nose and into the
brain. Then they search about for thoughts to eat.

STAGE 3
Thoughts are like tiny sparks of electricity. Microbats
stick their feathery heads into these sparks to feed.

Microbats like eating big ideas, but if they're hungry they'll eat any thoughts. Even boring thoughts about dust.

STAGE 1

A swarm of Microbats
flying up a nose.

STAGE 2

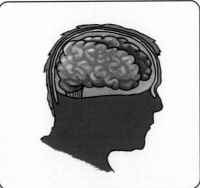

The brain. This is where
all your thoughts happen.

STAGE 3

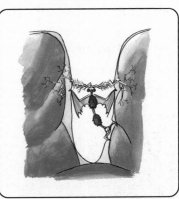

Look at that little thing
sucking up a thought.
Nasty!

The Microbat

Life Cycle

Microbats sleep in cats' armpits. They feed in brains and lay their eggs in snot.

Microbats lay eggs in human bogeys.

When the person sneezes, the eggs hatch out.

The baby Microbats dry off. Then they look for the nearest cat.

They sleep hanging from the cat's armpit hair.

They eat juicy thoughts in human brains.

Microbats die when they are fifty years old.

[Take a good look. The artist had to spend a week in snot to study those little guys.]

The Microbat

How to Spot One

This web page tells you all you need to know about spotting Microbats.

Internet sloth web finder - [yawn...]

Address | http://www.notarealwebsite.com/microbats/spotting_and_stopping.htm ▼

Microbats

They suck up your thoughts without asking.

You can tell you have them if...

- ...you can't remember a name.
- ...you forget the words to a song.
- ...you feel that your mind is blank.
- ...you have something really funny to say, but you can't remember what it is.

This is one of the horrible-looking things.

There are two ways to get rid of them...

1) Do the hardest sum you can find. This puts so much power through your brain that the Microbats get fried.

2) Get two people to play the recorder really badly either side of your head. Brothers and sisters love doing this.

Microbats can't stand bad recorder playing. Their heads just pop off like popcorn.

This will hurt, but it's a lot easier than maths.

The Hilltongue

The Hilltongue

The Hilltongue is a floating beast with a grassy back and 10,000 tongues.

A Hilltongue looks like a normal hill.

You might see a few of its tongues peeping out of the bottom if you look closely.

If you could look inside a Hilltongue, this is what you'd see.

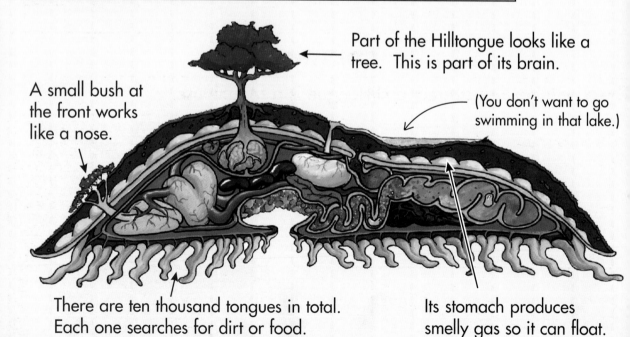

Part of the Hilltongue looks like a tree. This is part of its brain.

A small bush at the front works like a nose.

(You don't want to go swimming in that lake.)

There are ten thousand tongues in total. Each one searches for dirt or food.

(The tongues have soft hairs so they can slurp silently.)

Its stomach produces smelly gas so it can float.

The Hilltongue

Food

Hilltongues love eating dirt and any food or drink that comes in a tin.

BEFORE THE HILLTONGUE

AFTER THE HILLTONGUE

It looks like Hilltongues don't like tinned fish.

Enemies

The only thing that can eat a Hilltongue is a Moonlouse.

A Moonlouse is a massive thing that eats everything it crawls over.

Luckily Moonlice don't eat very often. The picture shows what one might look like if it came to Earth.

Find out more about the Moonlouse in the "Monsters from Space" book.

Catching Food

The Hilltongue sits on a house or village and licks it clean.

- Most of the time a Hilltongue will stay put, looking like a normal hill.
  But when a Hilltongue is hungry it lifts off the ground and goes hunting.

- When the Hilltongue finds a village, it sits down, covering it completely.
  The smell of a Hilltongue's breath makes everything in the village go to sleep.

- 10,000 tongues slowly lick up all the tinned food and all the dirt.

- When the Hilltongue moves on, everyone wakes up. Everything is very
  clean, but nobody can work out where all the tinned food has gone.

horrible
wallpaper

This picture was found hanging on a pub wall in Wiffledon.
It clearly shows a Hilltongue snoozing on a small school.

Little Hampton

The Hilltongue

Life Cycle

This timeline shows the full life cycle of a Hilltongue.

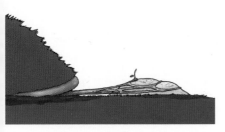

A baby Hilltongue

AGE (years)

 0 — Hilltongues are born as large molehills.

 4 — At the age of 4 they go around cleaning hedgehogs, foxes and badgers.

 16 — They get bigger and bigger until they start cleaning cows and cars.

 38 — Then sheds and elephants.

Cow wash
(like a car wash for cows)

 86 — Then houses.

 190 — Then villages.

 552 — At age 552 they retire to Scotland, Wales or Ireland.

A retirement home
for Hilltongues

How to Spot One

This newspaper shows two ways to spot a Hilltongue.

WEIRD TIMES

Number fourteen   WEDNESDAY JUNE 16 2004   40p

Sleeping Hilltongue shocker

Giant Hilltongue found sleeping on a Somerset School

Local drivers were shocked to find a hill where Tripton School used to be.

Regular readers of this paper will know what that means. Yes, 'Old Bill', the 150-year-old Hilltongue, is on the move.

Our Hilltongue expert, Ed Dening, explains what must have happened:

"Old Bill must have got hungry. He seems to be sitting on Tripton school. He'll be cleaning the school and the people in it as we speak."

Lucky escape for woodman

Warning. If you're chopping a tree and it bleeds, run, run, run.

Mr Martin was chopping down a tree when it started to bleed. He did exactly the right thing and made a run for it.

Local school goes grassy overnight.

MONSTER DETECTORS

HALF PRICE SALE NOW ON